This Walker book belongs to:

_____

_____

First published 1987
by Walker Books Ltd, 87 Vauxhall Walk, London SE11 5HJ

This edition published 2016

2 4 6 8 10 9 7 5 3 1

This book has been typeset in Bembo

Printed in China

British Library Cataloguing in Publication Data:
a catalogue record for this book is available from the British Library

ISBN 978-1-4063-7206-9

www.walker.co.uk

Spollyolly-diddlytiddlyitis
The Doctor Book

Michael Rosen   Quentin Blake

WALKER BOOKS

AND SUBSIDIARIES

LONDON · BOSTON · SYDNEY · AUCKLAND

Down at the Doctor's

Down at the doctor's
where everybody goes
there's a fat white cat
with a dribbly bibbly nose,
with a dribble dribble here
and a bibble bibble there,
that's the way
she dribbles her nose.

Down at the doctor's
where everybody goes
there's a fat black dog
with messy missy toes,
with a mess mess here
and a miss miss there,
that's the way
she messes her toes.

Down at the doctor's
where everybody goes
there's a fat red parrot
who everybody knows,
with a hi-de-hi here
and a how-de-how there,
that's the parrot
that everybody knows.

What If...

What if I went to the doctor's
and I was ill and I went into her little room
where she's got the toys in the corner
and she's lying on the bed
because she's ill
so she says,
"Hello, I'm really ill.
    What's wrong with me?"

So I pick up the stethoscope
and the thermometer
and all the other things on her desk
and I'm supposed to know what to do with them ...
and I do!

I do know,
I'm there with the stethoscope listening,
and I'm testing and feeling

and I'm saying, "Well, Doctor,
I'll tell you what's wrong with you.
You've got spollyollydiddlytiddlyitis,"

and she says, "Have I?"
And I say, "What you need is
a bottle of Rottybottytex."

And she says, "Thanks, thanks a lot.
Look, I've got some other sick people here,"
and she opens up a cupboard
and hundreds of ill people
walk out of the cupboard

and I'm testing and measuring and listening
for hours and hours, and all the time
it was me who was ill.

Things We Say

Nat and Anna

Nat and Anna sat in the waiting room with Mum.

Anna said, "When I grow up I'm going to be a doctor."

Nat said, "When I grow up I'm going to be a doctor."

Anna said, "I don't want you to be a doctor."

Nat said, "You can't stop me. Look, I'm a doctor."

Anna said, "No, you're not. You're Nat."

Nat said, "I'm Doctor Nat, the doctor."

Anna said, "So? I'm Doctor Anna."

Nat said, "I'm the doctor round here. You can be
a lorry driver."

Anna said, "I don't want to be a lorry driver."

Nat said, "You can be ill. You've got a headache."

Anna said, "I'm not playing this anymore, Nat."

Nat said, "I am. I'm Doctor Nat. I'm Doctor Nat."

Anna said, "You're not. You're Doctor Sick
because you're sick all the time."

Nat said, "I'm not sick all the time."
Anna said, "Doctor Sick Sick Sick."
Nat said, "You're getting really ill, Anna,
and I'm going to make you better."

Nat sat on Anna.

Anna said, "I'm not ill, I'm not ill, I'm not ill."
Mum looked up.
Mum said, "You are ill, Anna. That's why we've
come to see the doctor, okay?"

Nat said, "Anna is Doctor Sick."
Anna said, "Next time you're ill, Nat, I'm going to
be Doctor Jump and I'm coming to jump on you."
Nat said, "Oh don't, Anna."

Anna said, "Yes, I will. Jump jump jump all over you."

Nat sat and thought about Anna jumping on him.

Nat said, "Hey Anna. Look, let's both be ill, eh?"

Anna said, "No, let's both be Doctor Jump."

Feeling Ill

Lying in the middle of the bed
waiting for the clock to change
flicking my toes on the sheets
watching a plane cross the window
staring at the glare of the light
smelling the orange on the table
counting the flowers on the curtain
holding my head with my hand
hearing the steps on the stairs
lying in the middle of the bed
waiting for the clock to change.

This Woman Went to the Doctor's

This woman went to the doctor's and she said,
"Doctor, my family, we keep thinking we're all
sorts of different things."
"Like what?" said the doctor.
"Sometimes I feel like a cat."
"When did you start feeling like this?" said the doctor.
"When I was a kitten," she said.

"Oh, yes," said the doctor. "Anything else?"

"Well, my husband," she said, "he thinks he's a bell."

"Ah," said the doctor, "tell him to give me a ring. Anyone else?"

"Yes," said the woman, "my little boy. He thinks he's a chicken."

"Why didn't you tell me this before?" said the doctor.

"We needed the eggs," said the woman.

"Any other problems?" said the doctor.

"Yes, I keep forgetting things."

"What did you say?" said the doctor.

"I don't know," said the woman. "I've forgotten."

About the Author

Michael Rosen is one of the most popular authors of stories and poems for children. His titles include *We're Going on a Bear Hunt* (winner of the Smarties Book Prize), *Little Rabbit Foo Foo*, *Tiny Little Fly* and *Dear Mother Goose*. He has written many collections of poetry including *Let's Get Out of Here* and *Don't Put Mustard in the Custard*, both illustrated by Quentin Blake. He also compiled *Classic Poetry: An Illustrated Collection*. In 1997 he received the Eleanor Farjeon Award for services to children's literature and in 2007 he was appointed Children's Laureate.

About the Illustrator

Author photograph by Jacopo Moschin

Quentin Blake is a critically acclaimed children's book artist and was voted "The Illustrator's Illustrator" by *Observer* magazine. He is the illustrator of numerous Roald Dahl titles, several Michael Rosen poetry collections, *Michael Rosen's Sad Book* and *The Rights of the Reader* by Daniel Pennac. He has also created many acclaimed picture books of his own, including *Mr Magnolia* (winner of the Kate Greenaway Medal), *All Join In* (winner of the Kurt Maschler Award) and *Clown* (winner of Bologna Ragazzi Prize). In 1999 he was appointed the first Children's Laureate and in 2005 he was awarded a CBE for services to children's literature.